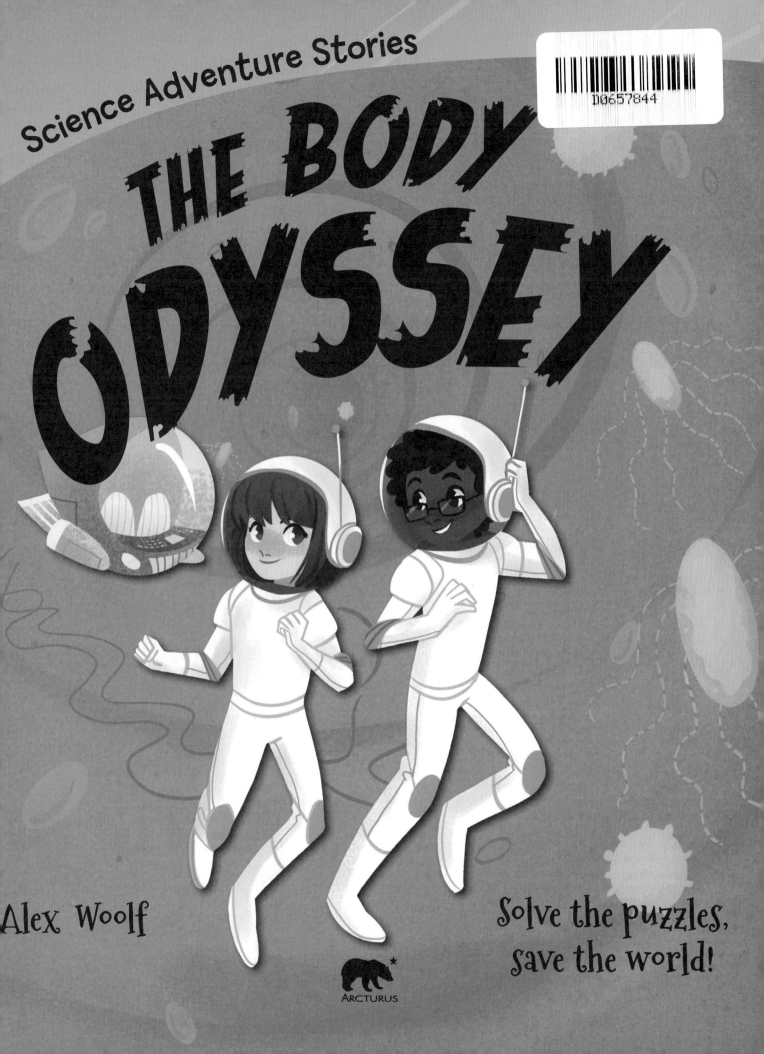

ARCTURUS

This edition published in 2020 by Arcturus Publishing Limited
26/27 Bickels Yard, 151–153 Bermondsey Street,
London SE1 3HA

Author: Alex Woolf
Illustrator: Geraldine Rodriguez
Editors: Rachel Cooke, Polly Goodman, and Joe Harris
Designers: Stefan Holliland and Emma Randall

ISBN: 978-1-83940-320-0
CH008100NT
Supplier 33, Date 0220, Print run 9664

Printed in China

SCIENCE TECHNOLOGY ENGINEERING MATHEMATICS

What is STEM?

STEM is a world-wide initiative
that aims to cultivate an
interest in Science, Technology,
Engineering, and Mathematics,
in an effort to promote these
disciplines to as wide a variety of
students as possible.

HOW TO USE THIS BOOK

This exciting, interactive adventure story features questions throughout. When you reach a question, stop! To unlock the next part of the story, you must find the right answer. <u>DON'T SKIP AHEAD</u> until you've worked it out! Check that your solution is correct by turning to the answers at the back of the book.

Watch for the DATA BLAST pages throughout. These are packed with science facts and explanations. Read them carefully, because they will help you answer the questions. If you don't know the answer to a question, turn back to the previous Data Blast page.

SAFETY WARNING

The stories in this book use exciting situations to illustrate important scientific principles. They are NOT intended as suggestions of activities for you to try at home. You should NOT attempt to shrink to the size of a blood cell, enter a human heart valve, or remove someone's appendix.

One day, schoolgirl Anna Tomical receives an unexpected call. "Who is it?" asks her friend Hugh. "It's my great-uncle, the world-famous scientist, Professor Barrington Bone!" The Professor summons them to his lab to see his latest invention.

How can we help?

Anna and Hugh rush to the lab. There, they are met not by Professor Bone, but by his assistant, Justin Jectem. Justin looks very worried. "The Professor's great rival, Belinda Blood, has injected a tiny robot into his bloodstream! It's made him very sick!"

This is the Microship.

"The only way to save Professor Bone is to use his latest invention, a Microship," says Justin. "It's a shrinking submarine that can travel inside people's bodies. You will need to pilot the Microship through his body, while I give you instructions."

Anna and Hugh climb on board the Microship, and Justin presses a button on a control panel in the lab. ZAAAAAP! Suddenly, the kids find themselves in a red tunnel.

"This must be a vein," says Anna. All around them are red blood cells, floating in a clear liquid. They hear Justin's voice crackling over an intercom system.

"To catch the "SickBot," you'll need to head for the heart."

Is it this way?

? Which way does blood travel in veins? Does it go to or from the heart?

If you don't know ... then turn the page for your first DATA BLAST! ?

Before you set off, let's refresh what you know about circulation. The Microship's computer will bring you up to speed!

CIRCULATION is the body's internal transport system. It includes the blood, blood vessels, and heart. Blood is made up of red and white blood cells, and platelets. They all float in a watery liquid called plasma.

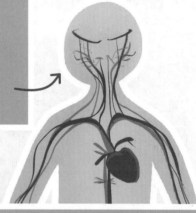

RED BLOOD CELLS carry oxygen to the body's cells, and carry carbon dioxide from the cells back to the lungs.

WHITE BLOOD CELLS fight disease. They work together to attack bacteria and viruses.

The HEART is the organ that pumps blood. It has four chambers—right atrium, right ventricle, left atrium, and left ventricle. Oxygen-poor blood from the body arrives in the right atrium, then moves to the right ventricle. From here it is sent along the pulmonary artery to the lungs to receive oxygen. The oxygen-rich blood then travels back to the heart's left atrium, passes to the left ventricle and then is pumped out to the rest of the body.

PLATELETS help blood to clot (become sticky) when you get a cut. They form a mesh over the wound that will eventually form a scab.

The blood cells and platelets float in a liquid called PLASMA. Plasma contains chemicals called antibodies, which help shield the body from disease.

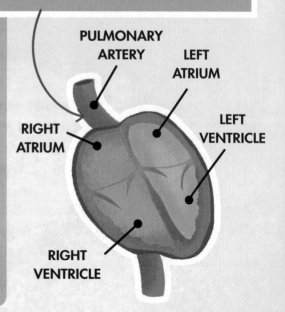

PULMONARY ARTERY

LEFT ATRIUM

LEFT VENTRICLE

RIGHT ATRIUM

RIGHT VENTRICLE

BLOOD VESSELS are tubes that carry blood. There are three types. Arteries carry blood away from the heart in fast surges. Veins carry blood back to the heart. Tiny, fine-branching blood vessels called capillaries link up the veins and arteries, and carry blood to and from the body's cells.

The Microship makes a sputtering noise. Hugh notices a flashing light on the control panel. "We'll need oxygen for fuel! But don't red blood cells carry oxygen?"

"Not always ... " says Anna. "They sometimes carry carbon dioxide."

Which gas do red blood cells carry in arteries to the body's cells? Which gas do they carry in veins from the cells back to the heart and lungs?

Just then, a white blood cell appears. These cells attack invaders ... including Microships!

"Look, there's a camouflage setting!" says Anna. "But what should we disguise ourselves as?"

Should they disguise the ship as a bacterium or an antibody?

In their new disguise, Anna and Hugh manage to escape the white blood cell.

Unfortunately, in all the excitement, they take a wrong turn. They race down narrow, branching passages, until the Microship gets stuck!

Push harder!

Eventually, Anna and Hugh free the Microship. "That's a relief," says Hugh. "But where are we? What is this vessel?"

Are they in a vein or an artery? Or somewhere else?

Anna and Hugh eventually manage to reach a larger blood vessel. The blood here is moving much faster than before, in powerful surges. But the Microship's blinking control panel says they are very low on fuel.

Justin's voice crackles over the intercom again. "Those blood cells are carrying oxygen," he says. "You could use them to refuel."

"But are we going the right way to get to the heart?" asks Anna.

What kind of blood vessel are they now in? Will it take them to the heart?

Bad news! They're in an artery, which means they are moving away from the heart.

They must return through the capillaries and find a vein. But something is wrong. The blood is rushing faster than usual. They see light ahead of them. Blood is pouring out of a hole in the skin!

What makes blood become sticky?

What things within blood help it clot?

Has Professor Bone grazed himself, or is this the work of the SickBot?

"It's okay," says Anna, "the blood will soon become sticky and form a mesh over the wound."

"That doesn't seem to be happening," says Hugh. "Something is wrong."

The SickBot has done something to Professor Bone's blood and it isn't clotting. Anna and Hugh must act quickly. They climb out of the Microship and begin pushing special parts of the blood to the wound site. Soon, a mesh has formed over the wound.

The mesh has stopped the bleeding, but it won't stop germs.

Don't worry. It hasn't finished changing yet!

What will the mesh turn into?

Leaving the graze behind, Anna and Hugh race along a vein to the heart.

"We need to catch the SickBot before it causes any more trouble!" says Anna.

If the SickBot has been interfering with the heart ...

... it could still be nearby!

How many chambers do we need to search?

How many chambers does the heart have? What are their names?

Anna and Hugh enter the heart's right atrium through a valve. From here they move swiftly through another valve into the right ventricle. However, they can't see the SickBot anywhere.

Suddenly, everything starts shaking. They can hear a deep coughing and choking. Professor Bone is struggling to breathe. The SickBot must have gone to his lungs!

"We're in the right ventricle of the heart," says Hugh. "But which chamber leads to the lungs?"

COUGH COUGH COUGH!

Which chamber of the heart leads to the lungs?

Another valve opens, pulling the Microship into a blood vessel.

"Wait!" shouts Anna. "The computer says this is the pulmonary artery. But does that lead to the lungs?"

"We have to decide quickly," cries Hugh. "We're getting dragged in there!"

Is this the right way?

My heart isn't set on it.

Where does the pulmonary artery lead?

Computer, can you tell us anything about the lungs?
The lungs are part of the body's RESPIRATORY SYSTEM. Here's what you need to know.

Breathing is essential to life. If we stopped breathing, we would die in just a few minutes. We breath in oxygen from the air. Our cells need oxygen to take energy from our food into our body. This process produces a waste gas called carbon dioxide. We breathe out to get rid of carbon dioxide. Another word for breathing is respiration. The parts of the body we use for breathing are called the respiratory system. They include the mouth, nose, throat, larynx, trachea, and lungs.

DATA BLAST

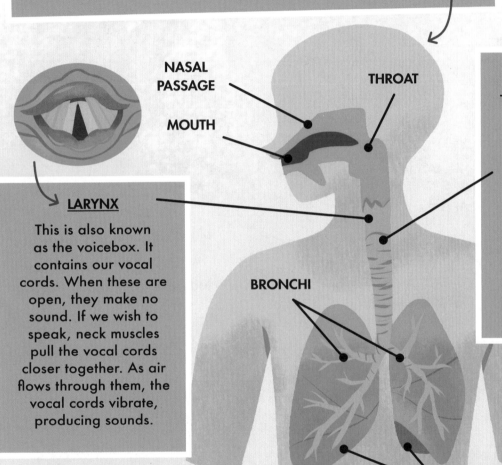

NASAL PASSAGE

THROAT

MOUTH

TRACHEA

This is also known as the windpipe. It is a hollow tube that connects the throat to the lungs. The trachea is lined with thousands of tiny hairs called cilia. These trap dust and other particles from the air, preventing them from reaching the lungs. When we cough, we force these particles out of the trachea.

LARYNX

This is also known as the voicebox. It contains our vocal cords. When these are open, they make no sound. If we wish to speak, neck muscles pull the vocal cords closer together. As air flows through them, the vocal cords vibrate, producing sounds.

BRONCHI

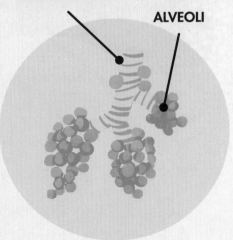

BRONCHIOLE

ALVEOLI

LUNGS

The trachea splits into two tubes called bronchi, one going to each lung. Inside the lungs, the bronchi divide into a network of smaller tubes called bronchioles. At the end of the smallest bronchioles are tiny, bumpy air sacs called alveoli (one is an alveolus). Wound around the alveoli are capillaries. These bring blood to the lungs to be recharged with oxygen from the alveoli (and then sent back to the heart for pumping around the body). The capillaries also release carbon dioxide into the alveoli to be breathed out. Alveoli and capillaries have walls thin enough for tiny gas molecules to pass through.

The Microship shoots along the pulmonary artery and enters a network of tiny capillaries. Finally, the kids find themselves looking at a hollow object with a bumpy surface, which keeps growing bigger, then smaller.

Anna and Hugh pilot the Microship through a capillary, right up to the hollow object ... but they can't get inside. There's a wall blocking their route!

I'm sure something is getting through the wall. It's causing the dark blood cells in this capillary to become bright red.

We saw bright-red blood cells before, when we were in the artery. They look like that when they're carrying a gas.

Have they reached the lungs? What is the name of the lumpy object that keeps expanding and shrinking?

So gases can move through the wall. To follow, we'll have to get even smaller!

Get ready to shrink to molecular size!

Anna presses the "shrink" button on the control panel. The Microship becomes even tinier, and passes through the wall of the alveolus. Once through, it expands again.

They are now inside the lungs' airways, and it's a very windy place! They keep getting blown about, but they manage to force their way out of the alveolus and into a series of narrow tubes.

These tubes are very narrow. Are we going the right way?

What are the tubes called? Where do they eventually lead?

This journey is a breeze without all that wind blowing.

I'm not sure that's a good thing. It may mean that Uncle Barrington isn't breathing.

Eventually they reach a wider tube called the bronchus. Then the wind stops blowing.

"This is an emergency!" calls Justin, over the intercom. "We have to get Professor Bone breathing again!"

Anna and Hugh race up the bronchus to reach an even wider tube, called the trachea. The SickBot is using some kind of forcefield to block the trachea, so no air can get through!

CRASH! Anna and Hugh ram the SickBot, and it goes flying up Professor Bone's throat and into his mouth.
He can breathe again!

"Quick! We can't let it get away!" says Hugh.

This is a pain in the neck!

But they can't follow the SickBot. They keep getting stuck on the hairy, sticky walls of the trachea.

What are these hairs and how can they escape them?

Anna presses a button in the Microship marked "Tickler." Professor Bone coughs, freeing them from the hairs.

COUGH COUGH!

The Microship flies upward and crashes against a pair of fleshy doors. Air from the lungs is flowing through the gap between the doors, causing them to vibrate and make a deep, complicated sound.

How can we make them open?

? ?

What are these doors? What is the sound they're making? Can you think of a way to open them?

"Uncle Barrington must be talking," says Anna. "Justin, you have to stop him! That will open the vocal cords."

Justin tells Professor Bone to rest his voice.

Shhh!

A moment later, the vocal cords open and the Microship passes through the throat and into the mouth. There's no sign of the SickBot!

Then they hear a deep gurgle from far below! The SickBot must have gone to the stomach. Before they follow, the ship's computer uploads some more important info …

MOUTH
THROAT
ESOPHAGUS
STOMACH
SMALL
INTESTINE
LARGE
INTESTINE

The body cannot use food as it is, so must break it down into simpler substances. This is called digestion. Most of the digestive system is a tube that travels through the body and includes the esophagus (also known as the foodpipe), stomach, small intestine, and large intestine. Other organs that help digestion include the liver and pancreas.

MOUTH AND FOODPIPE

The tongue tastes the food, teeth mash it, and saliva softens it. When the food is ready for swallowing, the tongue pushes it to the back of the mouth. The food touches the top of the throat, and this reflex reaction causes flaps to close off the windpipe, so the food moves into the esophagus, a muscular tube that sends it to the stomach.

PALATE
NASAL CAVITY
MOUTH
THROAT
TONGUE
ESOPHAGUS
LARYNX

STOMACH

This is a bag-like organ with wrinkled, muscular walls that stretch to make space for a meal. Glands in the stomach wall make an acidic liquid called gastric juice (stomach acid) that helps break down the food.

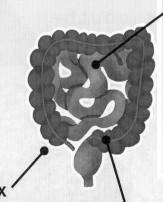

APPENDIX

SMALL INTESTINE

This is a long, narrow tube coiled up inside the abdomen. Here, juices produced by the liver and pancreas help to further break down food into useful nutrients. These are absorbed into the body through the lining of the small intestine. Juice from the pancreas also contains a chemical to protect the small intestine from stomach acid.

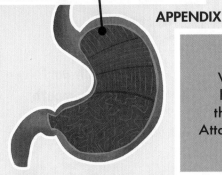

LARGE INTESTINE

What's left of the food is waste matter, which passes into the large intestine. Here, water is absorbed from the waste, and the remaining solids leave the body when you go to the toilet. Attached to the first part of the large intestine is a long, thin pouch called the appendix. This has no important function.

"We need to get to the stomach," says Anna.

"The Professor will have to swallow us," says Hugh. "Let's move to the back of the mouth."

Anna presses the accelerator, but the Microship doesn't move. "We seem to be stuck!" she says.

The Microship has become trapped between the tongue and the roof of the mouth.

"Oh, no!" says Hugh. "You need to make your uncle want to swallow us!"

"Computer," says Anna, "is there food on board?"

We could squirt some chocolate into Professor Bone's mouth.

Is that a joke?

If so, it's in the best possible taste!

Which part of the mouth is used for tasting?

Hugh pushes a button, and the ship jettisons its emergency candy supply.
"It's working!" cries Anna, as the tongue starts pushing them backward.
Up ahead they can see the foodpipe. But then everything stops.
"What happened?" asks Hugh. "Why isn't he swallowing us?"

What has to happen to make Professor Bone swallow them?

Anna guides the Microship forward until its nose touches the top of the throat. Suddenly, flaps close off the windpipe, and the Microship goes tumbling into the esophagus.

After a short ride, they arrive in a big, dark cave with wrinkled walls—the stomach!

We just needed to touch the top of the throat. Easy!

What liquid is being produced by the stomach? Is it dangerous?

What is that liquid? Will it harm us?

I don't think I have the stomach for this!

Bad news! The chocolate has made Professor Bone hungry, and he's grabbed a snack! An avalanche of cake pours down the esophagus. The stomach stretches to make room, and its walls start spraying liquid onto the cake.

Anna quickly activates a shield to protect the Microship from the powerful acid.

After about an hour, the cake has turned to a soft, soupy mush. A ring of muscle below them opens and they enter the long, narrow tube of the small intestine.

Anna catches a glimpse of the SickBot. It spots her too—and vanishes deeper into the tube!

"I wonder what it was doing?" Hugh says.

"Look," says Anna, "the walls of the intestine are being damaged by stomach acid. We have to try to help!"

The SickBot is doing something to the intestine walls.

What normally protects the intestine walls from stomach acid?

The SickBot's blocked the ducts from the pancreas so its protective juices aren't coming through.

They set to work unblocking the ducts. Soon, the pancreatic juice is flowing once again.

The journey through the small intestine takes a long time. The walls are lined with fingerlike structures called villi, filled with blood vessels that absorb the nutrients from the food. The Microship is not a nutrient, so it's free to continue on its way.

Finally, they enter the large intestine. They travel its length, but the SickBot is nowhere to be seen. "I wonder where it's hiding," says Anna.

Then they receive a text from Justin. "Professor Bone says his appendix is hurting. Please investigate!"

What and where is the appendix?

Anna and Hugh locate the appendix and quickly travel there.

"There's the SickBot!" says Anna.

The evil robot is sending out bad germs into the appendix, making it swell up. It looks painful for poor old Professor Bone!

Anna blocks up the entrance of the appendix with the Microship so the SickBot can't escape. Then they put on their diving helmets and swim down to the SickBot. Hugh distracts it while Anna finds the power switch, and switches it off.

Back aboard the Microship, they call Justin.

"Well done!" he says. "You've disabled the SickBot. However, the appendix is infected with germs that could spread to the rest of the body."

Anna has an idea. "Could the appendix be removed?"

Radical times call for radical solutions!

Is the appendix important?

Luckily, the appendix is not an important organ and it can be removed! Justin Jectem uses his surgical skills to operate on Professor Bone, removing his appendix, along with the Microship and the SickBot. "We did it!"

The following day, Belinda Blood makes a video call to Anna, Hugh and Justin. "By now, Professor Bone must be extremely sick!" she cackles. "With him gone, I'll take all the credit for his invention, the Microship! I'll be the world's most famous scientist!"

Just then, Professor Bone enters the room. "Sorry, Belinda," he says, "I'm actually feeling extremely well! Your plan was foiled, thanks to Anna, Hugh, Justin ... and my amazing Microship!"

ANSWERS

PAGE 5

Blood in veins goes from the body's cells to the heart. The blood is under less pressure in veins than it is in arteries, so the walls don't have to be as strong as artery walls.

PAGE 7

Red blood cells carry oxygen in arteries from the heart and lungs to the body's cells.

Red blood cells carry carbon dioxide in veins from the cells back to the heart and lungs.

They should camouflage themselves as an antibody. Antibodies are disease-fighting proteins in the blood, so would not be attacked. Bacteria are foreign bodies that will be attacked by white blood cells.

WHITE
BLOOD CELL

PAGE 8

They are in a capillary. Capillaries are very fine networks of blood vessels that carry blood through the tissues of the body.

PAGE 9

They are in an artery. It does not lead to the heart. It carries blood away from the heart to the body's cells.

PAGE 10

The things within blood that help it clot are called platelets. They are very tiny fragments of cells.

PAGE 11

The mesh will turn into a protective scab.

PAGE 12

The heart has four chambers—the right atrium, the right ventricle, the left atrium, and the left ventricle.

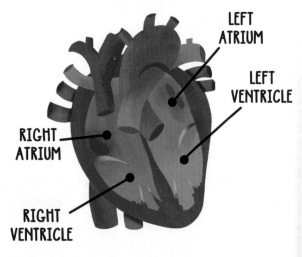

LEFT ATRIUM

LEFT VENTRICLE

RIGHT ATRIUM

RIGHT VENTRICLE

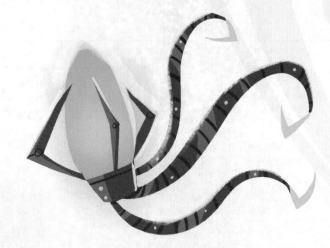

PAGE 16

Yes, they have reached the lungs. The chamber that keeps expanding and shrinking is an alveolus.

PAGE 13

The right ventricle of the heart leads to the pulmonary artery, which in turn leads to the lungs.

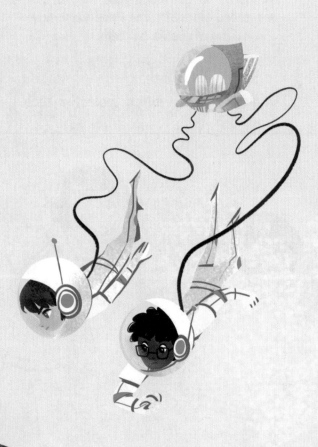

PAGE 17

The tubes are called bronchioles. They eventually lead to the bronchi and the trachea or windpipe.

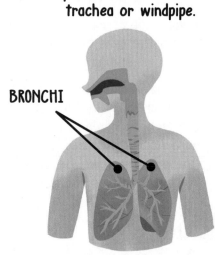

BRONCHI

PAGE 18

The hairs on the walls of the trachea are called cilia. They trap dust and other particles in the air that we breathe in. The body expels them by coughing. Anna and Hugh could free themselves by making the Prof. cough.

PAGE 19

The "doors" are vocal cords. The sounds they are making are speech. When we speak, the vocal cords close to a narrow gap. The air moving through the gap makes the vocal cords vibrate, creating speech sounds. Anna and Hugh can get them to open by asking Professor Bone to stop speaking.

VOCAL CHORDS

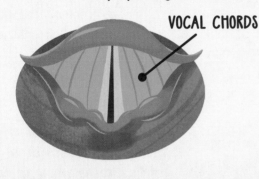

PAGE 22

The tongue is used for tasting. Its top surface contains clusters of special taste-sensitive cells called taste buds. When food touches these, it sends signals to the brain. The brain interprets these (along with smell signals sent by the nose) and works out what is being tasted.

PAGE 23

Swallowing is triggered by food touching the top of the throat. The Microship has to touch the top of Professor Bone's throat before he can swallow them. When it touches the top of his throat, this will produce a reflex reaction, pushing the Microship into the foodpipe.

PAGE 24

The liquid produced by the stomach is gastric juice. It contains a powerful acid to break down food and kill microorganisms, so it is dangerous to the Microship.

GASTRIC JUICES

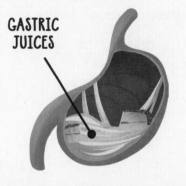

PAGE 25

The intestine walls are protected from stomach acid by pancreatic juice.

PAGE 26

The appendix is a sac attached to the large intestine near where it joins with the small intestine.

PAGE 27

The appendix does not have any important digestive function. It can safely be removed.

GLOSSARY

ALVEOLUS A tiny air sac in the lungs, through which oxygen is taken into the blood.

APPENDIX A small, closed tube attached to the digestive system.

ANTIBODY A substance produced in a body to destroy substances that carry disease.

ARTERY A thick tube that carries blood from your heart to the rest of your body.

ATRIUM The upper chamber of each half of the heart.

BACTERIUM A very small organism, some of which can cause disease.

CAPILLARY A delicate, thin-walled blood vessel.

CELL The smallest part of an animal or plant.

ESOPHAGUS Foodpipe or gullet, the tube through which food passes on its way to the stomach.

PANCREATIC JUICE A liquid released by the pancreas that contains enzymes important for digesting food.

PULMONARY ARTERY Artery that carries blood from the heart to the lungs for oxygenation.

RED BLOOD CELL A type of cell that carries oxygen and carbon dioxide to and from the body's tissues.

RESPIRATORY SYSTEM The parts of the body we use for breathing, including the mouth, nose, throat, larynx, trachea, and lungs.

SMALL INSTESTINE The narrow section of the intestines, extending from the end of the stomach to the large intestine, in which digestion is completed.

TRACHEA Windpipe, or tube that carries inhaled air to your lungs.

VEINS Thin tubes that carry blood towards your heart.

VENTRICLE Part of the heart that pumps blood to the arteries.

VILLI Numerous, fingerlike projections of the lining of the small intestine.

VOCAL CORDS Folds of tissue in the larynx, which vibrate and produce sound when air from the lungs is forced over them.

WHITE BLOOD CELL A type of cell that fights disease.

FURTHER INFORMATION

DK Publishing. *Knowledge Encyclopedia Human Body!* London, UK. DK Children, 2017

Elcomb, Ben and van Tulleken, Chris. *Operation Ouch!* London, UK. Puffin, 2017

INDEX